FRANZ SCHUBERT

QUARTET

for 2 Violins, Viola and Violoncello
E major / E-Dur / Mi majeur
D 353

Ernst Eulenburg Ltd

London · Mainz · Madrid · New York · Paris · Tokyo · Toronto · Zürich

Quartet

I

Franz Schubert, Op. 125 No. 2
1797 - 1828

Allegro con fuoco

Violino I

Violino II

Viola

Violoncello

E. E. 1219

Ernst Eulenburg Ltd

4

E.E.1219

E. E. 1219

8

E. E. 1219

8

210

dim. dim. dim. dim.

220

230

II.

III. Menuetto

Allegro vivace

E.E. 1219

Trio

Menuetto da Capo

IV. Rondo

Allegro vivace

E.E.1219

E. E. 1219

180

E.E.1219

190

200

32

34